Traffic Signs Manual

Department of The Environment,
Transport and the Regions

Scottish Development Department

Welsh Office

London: The Stationery Office

Traffic Signs Manual 1982

Contents of Chapters 1-8

* To be published

Published for The Department of the Environment, Transport and the Regions under licence
from the Controller of Her Majesty's Stationery Office.

First published 1982
Fourth impression 1999
First edition Crown Copyright 1977

ISBN 0 11 550559 8

Printed in the United Kingdom for The Stationery Office
J77951 4/99 C5 10170

Foreword

1. In 1963 the Traffic Signs Committee under the Chairmanship of Sir Walter Worboys, presented its report to the Secretary of State for Scotland and the then Minister of Transport whose responsibilities on highway matters at that time covered Wales as well as England.

2. The report recommended the introduction of entirely new traffic signs on all-purpose roads and suggested the introduction of an illustrated manual to provide advice and guidance on their use.

3. The new signs were first prescribed in the Traffic Signs Regulations and General Directions 1964 which came into operation on 1 January 1965. The 1964 Regulations have since been revoked by the Traffic Signs Regulations and General Directions 1975 which have in turn been revoked by the Traffic Signs Regulations and General Directions 1981.

4. It was expected that the Traffic Signs Manual would take a long time to prepare and publish and therefore the green booklet *Informatory Signs for use on All-purpose Roads* was published in 1964 to encourage the early introduction of some of the new signs. In addition to dealing comprehensively with the subject of Informatory Signs, the booklet included the design rules for the new signs and gave guidance on such matters as their mounting and siting. Although much of the information given in *Informatory Signs for use on All-purpose Roads* is still relevant, readers should now read it in conjunction with the revised design rules and advice given in the joint Departmental Circular numbered, Department of the Environment Circular Roads No: 7/75, Scottish Development Department Circular No: R332 and Welsh Office Circular No: 54/75.

5. The Manual itself was originally planned and published in separate chapters as loose-leaf publications for insertion into the Traffic Signs Manual binder. It was thought that this form of publication would facilitate the revision of the manual as and when required. Amendments and revised texts could be introduced simply by an exchange of pages. Unfortunately the amendment system has been wholly frustrated by administrative and distributive difficulties and consequently it has been found necessary when revising chapters or bringing them up-to-date, to re-write each Chapter as a whole. In these circumstances and to meet the needs of individuals and individual organisations whose interests may be confined to a single chapter, it has been decided to abandon the loose-leaf format and to publish all revised and hitherto unpublished chapters when required as individually bound publications.

6. The chapter contents of the complete Traffic Signs Manual are listed opposite. The chapters marked with an asterisk are currently available in the form of individually bound publications and future publications of chapters of the Traffic Signs Manual will be notified in official circulars issued either individually or jointly by the three Departments concerned.

7. Enquiries regarding the Traffic Signs Manual may be made through the appropriate Regional Controller (R&T) or direct to the Traffic Engineering Division of the Department of Transport.

Department of Transport
Scottish Development Department
Welsh Office

1982

CHAPTER 1

Introduction

CHAPTER 1
Contents

Note:

The Traffic Signs Manual is equally applicable in England, Scotland and Wales and references to the *Secretary of State* should be interpreted as referring to either the Secretary of State for Transport in England, the Secretary of State for Scotland or the Secretary of State for Wales, as appropriate.

References to the Regional Controller (R&T) should be interpreted as referring to the Assistant Chief Engineer, the Greater London Roads and Traffic Division, the Chief Road Engineer Scottish Development Department, or the Director of Highways of the Welsh Office Transport and Highways Group, as appropriate.

1. Introductory

TURN LEFT
Regulatory (Mandatory) Sign

PEDESTRIANS PROHIBITED
Regulatory (Prohibitory) Sign

BEND TO THE RIGHT AHEAD
Warning Sign

**Advance Directional
Informatory Sign**

Quick recognition of different groups of signs is aided by the use of different shapes and colours

1.1 Clear and efficient signing is an essential part of highway and traffic engineering and a road with poor signing or with badly maintained signs is an unsatisfactory road. Road users depend on signing for information and guidance; highway authorities depend on signing for the efficient working and the enforcement of traffic regulations, for traffic control, and as an aid to road safety. Signing includes not only signs on posts but also carriageway markings, beacons, studs, bollards, traffic signals and other devices.

1.2 Signs must give road users their message clearly and at the correct time. The message must be unambiguous and speedily understood; it must be given not too soon for the information to have been forgotten before it is needed, and not too late for the safe performance of consequent manoeuvres.

1.3 The types of signs and carriageway markings etc, available for use are prescribed by Regulations. Limiting the number of types of sign available assists in their quick recognition as does uniformity of shape, colour and lettering for each type. It also makes available to highway authorities a set of standard signs and saves them the labour of design. It aids the courts in giving the same meaning to standard signs. Quick recognition is further aided by using different shapes and colours for different sign groups, eg, warning signs are triangular with black symbols, white grounds and red borders.

1.4 Uniformity of signs is not however enough; uniformity of signs without uniformity in use is objectionable and could impair road safety. For instance, warning signs sited at different distances from their hazards in different districts could confuse a road user accustomed to only one district.

1.5 To obtain the fullest benefits of uniformity there must not only be uniformity of signs but also uniformity in their use, in their siting and their illumination.

1.6 This manual sets out the codes to be followed in the use, siting, and illumination of signs both on all-purpose roads and motorways. It also covers temporary signs for use in connection with road works, in emergency by the police, and temporary route signing by motoring organisations and highway authorities.

1.7 In this chapter, after historical and legal sections, there follow sections describing the basic technical requirements of the present signing system. Most of these technical sections are expanded in greater detail in later chapters.

2. Historical

The internationally recognised STOP sign was first prescribed for use in the United Kingdom by the Traffic Sign Regulations and General Directions 1975.

1.8 The signs for all purpose roads described in this manual are based on the recommendations of the Report of the Traffic Signs Committee dated 18 April 1963. This report is widely known as the *Worboys Report*, taking its name from the Committee Chairman, Sir Walter Worboys.

1.9 The report, the main points of which were accepted officially, recommended the radical and urgent modernisation of the traffic signing system in the United Kingdom and resulted in the introduction of a whole new range of signs for use on all purpose roads. Apart from a few points of minor detail, motorway signs were not affected since their design at that time was comparatively new and accorded with the recommendations of the Report published in December 1960 of Sir Colin Anderson's Committee.

1.10 Generally, the design of *Worboys* signs closely followed the protocol on road signs proposed by the UN World Conference on road and motor transport held in Geneva in 1949. The 1949 Protocol was overtaken by the preparation in Vienna, in 1968, of a World Convention on Traffic Signs and Signals which was signed on behalf of over 60 countries including the United Kingdom. The signing of the Convention indicated the intention of the signatories to implement its recommendations at a future date. Then followed, as provided for in the Convention, a European regional agreement on traffic signs and signals together with a protocol on road markings. This regional agreement and the protocol, supplement the World Convention and provide for certain options to be used in the same way throughout Europe. They also contain some extra signs, markings and provisions covering matters on which either the Convention is silent or leaves on an optional basis. The United Kingdom has indicated its intention to implement both the agreement and the protocol subject to certain reservations. Adherence to the World Convention and its supplementary agreements by participating nations, particularly those in Europe, has resulted in a degree of uniformity in Traffic Signing, which is of obvious benefit to international travellers.

1.11 The *Worboys* signs were prescribed for the first time under the Traffic Signs Regulations and General Directions 1964, which were superseded by the Traffic Signs Regulations and General Directions 1975, which have now been superseded by the Traffic Signs Regulations and General Directions 1981.

3. Legal Aspects and Responsibilities for Signs

1.12 A full and comprehensive guide to the legal aspects of traffic signs is outside the scope of this manual. Legal matters are dealt with only briefly in this section.

1.13 Highway Authorities are responsible for ensuring correct standards of signing on their roads; only they can erect traffic signs or permit their erection. The Police also have certain responsibilities which are described later.

1.14 In England and Wales however, (excluding Scotland), it is the local authority which may not necessarily be the highway authority, which is responsible for erecting and maintaining waiting restriction and speed limit signs and for establishing pedestrian crossings in their area.

1.15 Authorities may only use signs—including carriageway markings—of a size, colour and type prescribed or specially authorised by the Secretary of State. The prescribed signs are included in *The Traffic Signs Regulations and General Directions 1981* Statutory Instrument 1981 No 859 and *The Traffic Signs (Speed Limits) Regulations and General Directions 1969* Statutory Instrument 1969 No 1487. These Statutory Instruments may be amended from time to time.

1.16 All the prescribed signs and carriageway markings are described in subsequent chapters of this manual. If an authority wishes to use a sign not prescribed in Regulations, application should be made to the appropriate Regional Controller (R&T) giving reasons for wanting a new sign and describing it in detail, preferably with drawings and site plans. The design of such signs should conform to Worboys principles. Only in exceptional circumstances will special signs be authorised. This is essential in order to keep the number of sign types to the absolute minimum required for the safe and efficient functioning of the road system. Any appreciable diversifications or increase in sign types having only local usage and significance can cause difficulties to road users unaccustomed to the area.

1.17 Authorities are not free to use all the signs shown in this manual at will without further authorisation. They may do so generally with informatory signs and warning signs, but there are a large number of signs which first require an Order to be made and some signs cannot be used without specific site approval of the Secretary of State. Subsequent chapters of this manual state where an Order or other authority is required before the sign can be used.

1.18 The use on Public highways of non-prescribed signs which have not been authorised by, or on behalf of, the Secretary of State, is illegal and Authorities who so use unauthorised signs act beyond their powers. Additionally, an unauthorised sign in the highway is an obstruction. The possible consequences of erecting or permitting the erection of obstructions may be severe and those responsible could lay themselves open to a claim for damages; for example if the obstruction is the cause of accident or of injury in a collision or if the unauthorised sign injuriously affects a fronting property by blocking light or impairing visual amenity.

1.19 Authorities will normally erect their traffic signs within the highway boundary. If this is not possible, they can erect signs on or over land adjacent to the highway with the owners' permission. They can also, if necessary, acquire land or rights over land either by agreement or compulsorily for the accommodation of signs.

1.20 Authorities should consider requiring the removal of any object or device erected privately on land adjacent to their roads which has the apparent or express intention of guiding, warning or directing road users.
In addition, private advertisements should not resemble or incorporate prescribed traffic signs or their symbols. United Kingdom signs are crown copyright and may not be reproduced without permission. In no circumstances will the Department permit the use of traffic signs on advertisements at road side locations. When prescribed traffic signs are used illegally action should be taken to secure their removal.

1.21 Certain comments on statutory requirements are also made in subsequent chapters as appropriate. References to advertisements in England and Wales are made in the Ministry of Housing and Local Government Circular No 11/62 and in Scotland in the Department of Health for Scotland Circular No 57/61 (Scotland).

1.22 The Secretary of State has overriding powers to require the removal or to remove any traffic sign or any object or device for the guidance or direction of persons using roads.

4. The Functions and Classification of Signs

1.23 Signs are used to control and guide traffic and to promote road safety. They should only be used where they can usefully serve these functions. Warning signs will not, for instance, promote road safety if used widely where there is no unusual degree of danger. On the other hand their omission where guidance, control or danger warrants the use of a sign is not in the best interests of road users.

1.24 The advice given in subsequent chapters of the manual should therefore be closely followed.

1.25 Apart from carriageway markings and temporary signs there are three main classes of road signs. Each class has its basic shape and as explained in later chapters the use of certain colours is restricted to particular classes of signs. The three classes are:

(i) Regulatory Signs
These include all signs which give notice of requirements, prohibitions or restrictions. They may be either mandatory or prohibitory. Regulatory signs are basically circular in shape and may be supplemented by plates beneath them augmenting the message given by the sign.

(ii) Warning signs
These signs give warning of a hazard ahead. The design of most warning signs is based on an equilateral triangle having its apex uppermost. They are sometimes supplemented by rectangular plates giving additional information as may be necessary.

(iii) Informatory signs
These signs normally give road users information about the route and about places and facilities of particular value or interest. Most informatory signs are rectangular but direction signs usually have one end pointed.

5. The Design and Use of Signs

1.26 In order to perform the function for which it is intended a sign must be capable of transmitting its message clearly and at the right time to road users travelling at the normal speed for the road. To achieve this a sign must have correct legibility distance, appropriate target value, simplicity of content and layout and effective illumination or reflectorisation. Signs must be adequate in design and construction without being extravagantly expensive.

1.27 The legibility of traffic signs is of prime importance. Its achievement depends mainly on the size of the lettering or the symbols used, although the use of adequate colour contrast between lettering and/or symbols and their background and the type of alphabet used are also important contributory factors.

1.28 Target value depends on both the colour and the size of the sign: a big sign will have adequate target value whatever its colour; but difficulties may arise with the smaller signs in urban areas in selecting sites with backgrounds which do not nullify the target value of the sign.

1.29 For simplicity of content and layout, ideographic representation of the message is most effective, but where lettering has to be used the message needs to be condensed into as few immediately comprehensible words as possible. Abstract symbolism is less satisfactory since its meaning must be learnt and remembered. In suggesting designs for signs to be specially authorised highway authorities should avoid abstract symbolism.

1.30 Size is the most important factor determining sign cost, therefore signs are designed to give the required legibility without wasting space.

1.31 Factors which determine the distance at which a sign should be legible at a given speed of travel are:

(a) the lateral clearance between the sign and the edge of carriageway and,

(b) the length of time needed for reading and absorbing the message. Drivers should not have to divert their eyes more than ten degrees away from the road ahead. This means that the message on a sign must be fully absorbed before a driver reaches the point where the observation angle exceeds ten degrees. If, as may be assumed, a driver needs a certain time to absorb a sign's message, the faster the speed of approach the further away must the reading of the sign commence. Reading must be completed and the message absorbed before reaching the point where concentration on a sign would distract attention too far from the road ahead.

1.32 These considerations have led to the design of signs of different sizes to suit different speed values. For directional and informatory signs where the legibility of the words is most important different sizes of alphabet are used. For ideographic and symbolic signs the size of the sign is proportional directly to the approach speed of traffic. In subsequent chapters details of these different sizes are given.

1.33 The lettering chosen for nearly all road signs is lower case with initial capitals. There is one alphabet for use with light lettering on a dark background and a second for dark lettering on a light background. A range of numerals, separators and other characters is also available for each alphabet.

1.34 There is additionally a special range for the route numbers on motorway signs.

More details of these alphabets are given in Chapter 2 and Circular Roads 7/75.

1.35 In addition to distinctive shapes, different classes of signs have distinctive colour combinations. The number of different colours which can be usefully used on signs is limited by both aesthetic and technical requirements; Appendix 1 lists the colours with their specifications. Subsequent chapters describe their use in detail.

1.36 With standardisation of types of signs, there must also be uniformity in the use, siting, mounting height, illumination and reflectorisation of signs within limitations imposed by site conditions.

1.37 As already emphasised uniformity in the use of signs is of first importance and is dealt with in detail in later chapters.

1.38 The Regulations and Directions, Statutory Instrument 1981 No. 859, limit the use of certain signs and certain classes of signs. The Traffic Signs Manual not only explains in non-legal language the requirements of the Regulations and Directions but also advises on all aspects of signs and their uses including matters not covered in the Statutory Instrument. If all highway authorities follow this advice a reliable and uniform system of traffic signing will be ensured and this will benefit road users throughout the United Kingdom.

6. The Positioning of Signs

1.39 There are four aspects to the positioning of a traffic sign:

(i) Its siting along the road in relation to the junction, hazard, or other feature to which it applies.

(ii) Its placement in relation to the edge of the carriageway and other features of the cross section.

(iii) Its height above the road and

(iv) Its orientation.

(i) Siting

1.40 In order to allow a driver adequate time to comply safely with its message each sign should be sited at the correct distance before the site to which it relates. This distance will generally depend on the speed value of the road.

1.41 Because signs are designed for the legends to be recognisable and legible from distances depending on their type and the road speed, it is obviously essential to ensure that the signs are in fact visible from these distances and not obscured by intervening obstructions.

1.42 In subsequent chapters details are given of such siting and visibility distances.

1.43 Drivers are accustomed to signs being on the left-hand side and such positioning should be the general practice.

1.44 However, siting on the right-hand side is appropriate in certain circumstances. For example where there are difficulties in siting on the left, or when worthwhile economies are to be gained such as at T junctions where one sign facing both ways will suffice instead of a sign on the left for each approach. At sharp left-hand bends siting on the right may not only be appropriate but preferable.

1.45 The right-hand side siting of signs is sometimes appropriate where signs need to be erected on both sides of a carriageway on one way streets, for example the NO ENTRY sign is normally so duplicated and on high speed dual carriageway roads duplication of warning signs is recommended. Duplication of speed limit signs is a statutory requirement—see Chapter 9.

1.46 Other methods of siting are sometimes required. For instance signs are usually placed on the far side of the head of the T junction for drivers approaching on the stem. At underpasses overhead signs may be more appropriate. Signs on roundabouts and refuges are also specially sited.

1.47 More guidance is given on detailed siting in the relevant parts of subsequent chapters.

(ii) Placement

1.48 Signs should be set at least 450mm from the edge of the carriageway. This should be increased to 600mm where there is a severe camber or crossfall and where signs are mounted on the central reserve of dual carriageways. On high-speed dual carriageway roads the clearance should be at least 1200mm and where there is a hardened verge the nearest edge of the sign should be not less than 600mm behind the edge of the hardening.

(iii) Mounting heights

1.49 Where possible the lower edge of the sign should be between 900mm and 1500mm above the highest point of the carriageway alongside. The higher mounting should be used where excessive spray is likely to soil the signs. In built up areas signs may have to be higher for various reasons where they are erected on footways and transverse to them they must obviously allow sufficient clearance for pedestrians: 2100mm is the minimum recommended but 2150mm or 2300mm is preferable.

(Note: In the areas of the former Scottish Burghs, the Burgh Police (Scotland) act 1892 requires signs to be 8ft above any footway).

1.50 If signs are to be illuminated externally by their own lamps and vandalism is likely, the signs must be sufficiently high for the lamps to be out of easy reach.

(iv) Orientation

1.51 In rural areas specular reflection from traffic signs can be troublesome. To eliminate or minimise its effect, signs should be set at angles so as to face slightly away from the beam direction of headlights from approaching vehicles within a distance of 200 metres.

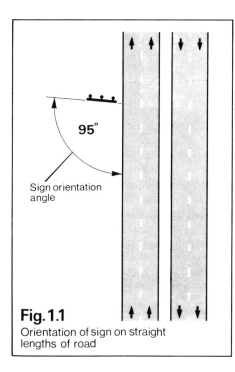

Fig. 1.1

Orientation of sign on straight lengths of road

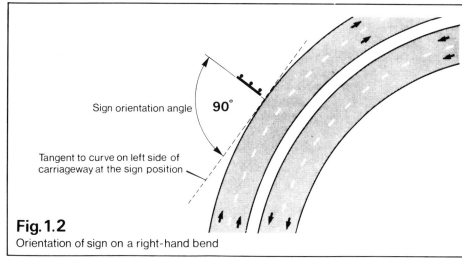

Fig. 1.2

Orientation of sign on a right-hand bend

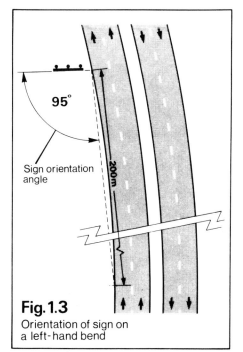

Fig. 1.3

Orientation of sign on a left-hand bend

On a straight length of road the horizontal axis of a sign should be set at an angle of 95° away from the general alignment of the left side edge of carriageway on the approach side (see fig. 1.1). On some bends and complicated winding alignments, compromise solutions may have to be adopted but generally it will be adequate on a right-hand bend for a sign to be set at an angle of 90° to a line tangential to the left-hand edge of the carriageway at the point where the sign is erected (fig. 1.2). Signs sited on left-hand bends should be set an an angle of 95° measured clockwise from a line joining the edge of the carriageway at the sign with a point on the same edge of carriageway 200 metres in advance of the sign (fig. 1.3).

1.52 Signs are normally to be set transverse to the line of travel of approaching road users. The main exceptions to this are the plates detailing the hours of waiting restrictions, which should be parallel to the kerb and some direction signs because they must point approximately to the direction to be taken.

1.53 For speed limits and traffic regulation Orders terminal signs will have to be placed at the ends of the lengths of road to which the Orders apply. As the signs must be obeyed they must be placed in a position of good visibility. It follows therefore that the lengths of restrictions themselves may be influenced by the best sign positions and before Orders are made due consideration should be

given to the precise siting of terminal signs. This should not be done in such a manner that appreciable lengths of unnecessary restrictions result.

1.54 In siting signs the advice given in subsequent chapters should be closely followed although it will not always be possible to adhere precisely to these standards due to site limitations. Variations in distance of up to 10% are generally permissible, but if an appreciably greater variation seems required other alternatives should first be investigated. Steps should be taken to deal with obstructions to the visibility of signs. Over-hanging trees and shrubs should be cut back and bus stops moved if necessary. Standing vehicles may have to be prohibited if the sign cannot be sited to be free from such obstruction.

1.55 Permanent features which cannot be altered such as bends, hill crests, narrow verges, buildings etc will necessitate the special siting of signs. It is preferable to increase the standard distance between the sign and the site to which it relates rather than diminish it, but such increase should not be more than the 10% tolerance mentioned in paragraph 1.54. If a suitable site cannot be found within these tolerances, then a decrease should be investigated. Terminal signs should be placed at or as close as practicable to the point specified in the relevant Order.

1.56 At all times correct visibility distances of the sign should be maintained. It is particularly important to ensure that growing vegetation, subsequent building development and other features such as shop signs and blinds do not obscure road signs.

7. Mounting Signs

1.57 It is desirable to limit the number of posts in footways, especially in urban areas, because proliferation creates additional hazards for visually handicapped pedestrians and unnecessary obstructions for people with perambulators and wheelchairs. Where possible signs should be attached to adjacent walls, so that they are not more than 2 metres from the edge of the carriageway, or be grouped on posts in accordance with paragraphs 1.62 – 1.68. Certain signs with small letters, eg plates for waiting restrictions, must always be mounted close to the edge of the carriageway. When posts must be erected in narrow footways they should be positioned to cause the least possible obstruction and should not reduce the clear walkway width to less than 1.0 metre.

1.58 Sign posts should be designed to accommodate the total area of signs to be attached to them. The attachment of larger or additional signs, to existing posts, should only be done after checking the adequacy of the strength of the posts, taking account of any reduction in strength due to corrosion. When existing posts are inadequate for the total loading they should be replaced rather than use additional posts for new signs. Lighting columns are normally not designed to accommodate the wind loading from signs attached to them. Signs should therefore never be attached to lighting columns unless:

(a) The columns, with signs attached, have been specifically designed to BS 5649 and the relevant Departmental Standard.

or (b) The adequacy of the columns with signs attached have been checked in accordance with BS 5649 and the relevant Departmental Standard. For existing lighting columns the design check should take account of the structural condition of the column.

Attachment of signs to lighting columns should be by external circumferential clamps which will not damage the column or its protective coating.

1.59 Purpose-made metal posts should preferably be tubular and of uniform diameter along their length; they should not project above the sign or lighting unit. Where possible the mounting should allow an angular movement for the adjustment of the sign before locking in its final position. Where enlargement of a post is needed to house control equipment it should be provided at the base of the post.

1.60 The very large signs used on high speed roads will require specially designed concrete or steel posts and the signs themselves will have to be strongly braced or framed. The mounting of the lighting units will also need special attention.

1.61 The colour of posts for signs must normally be grey; posts for pedestrian crossing beacons, hazard markers, and load gauges are black and white, whilst those for temporary traffic signals should either be grey or yellow, (see Appendix I). Concrete supports retain their natural colour. The backs of signs and bracing must be grey as should the fixing clips where these are painted. Full details of posts and supports are given in Chapter 13.

1.62 Generally, not more than two signs should be erected on any one post. Where a sign requires a supplementary plate, the combination of sign and plate may be regarded as one sign. Exceptionally, three signs may be mounted on one post provided none requires a supplementary plate.

1.63 A warning sign or signs must not be mounted on the same post with either the Stop or Give Way signs. Sign combinations which may be mounted together should be placed in the following order from top to bottom:

(a) Stop or Give Way or any triangular warning sign or signs.
(b) Speed limit signs.
(c) Other circular signs.
(d) Rectangular signs.

1.64 Generally, no assembly should exceed 4 metres in overall height above ground level, but this may be exceeded to obtain visibility of the signs at particularly difficult sites.

1.65 All proposed assemblies should be critically examined to ensure that the intended messages are clear and that there is no ambiguity, particularly where a supplementary plate with the legend 'End' is used to indicate the termination of a prohibition or restriction.

1.66 Where a speed limit sign is erected on the same post as a clearway sign accompanied by an *End* plate, the plate should be butted directly up to the base of the clearway sign. The speed limit sign should be mounted at the top of the assembly with space equal to twice the width of the red border between the roundels to ensure that there is no ambiguity.

1.67 Where rectangular signs are mounted together or a supplementary plate is mounted below a triangular sign, the signs should be separated by a space equal to the x-height of the lettering on the lower sign. In all other cases signs may be butted together one above the other.

1.68 Where two or more warning signs are to be erected together the sign relating to the hazard first encountered should be placed uppermost.

8. Sign Backgrounds

1.69 Signs may lose their effectiveness because of their setting. Some of the smaller signs may fail to stand out against a background which is variegated and colourful and others may be overpowered by a stronger background.

1.70 Advertisements behind or near signs may prove distracting; flashing or brilliantly illuminated ones may cause road users to miss signs.

1.71 These points should be borne in mind both when siting new Traffic Signs and in the exercise of the control of advertisements under the planning regulations.

1.72 Where it is impossible to avoid a poor or distracting background it may be partially screened by a backing board to the sign. Such boards should be black and their size should suit local conditions.

Note: Such boards should not be confused with:
(i) Backing boards used in connection with pedestrian crossings and traffic signals which are black with white border.

(ii) Boards used for mounting two or more Signs together as an assembly, which should be coloured grey.

9. Maintenance of Signs

1.73 Signs must at all times be maintained so as to preserve their original effectiveness and general condition. It is a waste of public money to provide signs and then to allow them to lose effectiveness by subsequent deterioration.

1.74 Signs become less effective not only when characters or colouring deteriorate, but also when dirty or damaged or displaced as a result of accidents or vandalism. Damaged or dirty signs discredit the highway authority and lessen road users' respect for the signs. A periodic inspection of signs should be made to ensure their early repair and/or replacement when necessary and after dark inspections should be made of illuminated or reflectorised signs.

1.75 Regular cleaning of all signs is essential. No firm advice can be given about frequency of cleaning since dirt deposition varies with the district, the climate, the time of the year and the position of the signs.
Illuminated or reflectorised signs soon lose their effectiveness if damaged or dirty. Local conditions will also govern the methods of cleaning.

1.76 Further advice is given in Chapter 12.

10. Specification for Signs

1.77 Specifications for construction of signs, bollards and their supports are contained in the current edition of *British Standard No 873, The Construction of Road Traffic Signs and Internally Illuminated Bollards.* No signs should be purchased unless they comply with this standard in all appropriate respects.

1.78 Further information is given in Chapter 13.

11. Illumination and Reflectorisation of Signs

1.79 The requirements for the illumination and/or reflectorisation of traffic signs as laid down in the Regulations, together with advice on equipment, methods of lighting etc, are given in Chapter 11 and Advice Note TA/19/81 "Reflectorisation of Traffic Signs". Site checks should be made during darkness to ensure that reasonable visibility standards are achieved and if a reflectorised only sign at a particular location does not perform adequately, it may be directly illuminated.

1.80 For reflectorised signs, button reflectors may only be used on round hazard markers. Reflectorisation on most other types of signs must be *whole area* reflectorisation (see Regulations 17, 18 and 19 Traffic Signs Regulations and General Directions 1981).

Standard Colours to be used for Signs, Posts and Fittings

Red	British Standard 381C No 537 (Signal Red)
Blue	British Standard 381C No 109 (Middle Blue)
*Yellow	British Standard 381C No 355 (Lemon)
Green for primary route signs	British Standard 381C No 226 (Middle Brunswick Green)
Green for Fire Rendezvous Point and Traffic Signals Ahead signs	British Standard 381C No 225 (Light Brunswick Green)
Grey for posts, fittings and backs of signs	British Standard 381C No 693 (Aircraft Grey)
Orange	British Standard 381C No 557 (Light Orange)
Black	As specified in British Standard 873, 1.3.3
White	As specified in British Standard 873, 1.3.2

*Note:
The standard colour for waiting and loading restriction lines is BS 381C
No 355 (lemon), but in environmentally sensitive areas No 310 (primrose)
or No 353 (deep cream) may be used for these lines.